S0-ATZ-212

ILLUMINATION PRESENTS

DESPICABLE ME 3 ™

Jumbo
Coloring and Activity Book

UNIVERSAL
A COMCAST COMPANY

ILLUMINATION
ENTERTAINMENT

www.despicable.me   #DespicableMe

Despicable Me 3 is a trademark and copyright of Universal Studios. Licensed by Universal Studios. All Rights Reserved.

bendon®

© 2017 Bendon. The BENDON name, logo and Tear & Share are trademarks of Bendon Ashland, OH 44805.

BUST A MINION

TM & © Universal Studios

Break the Secret Code

Use code key to decipher the message.

CODE KEY												
11	21	31	41	51	61	71	81	91	01	12	13	14
A	B	C	D	E	F	G	H	I	J	K	L	M
15	16	17	18	19	10	27	37	47	57	67	77	87
N	O	P	Q	R	S	T	U	V	W	X	Y	Z

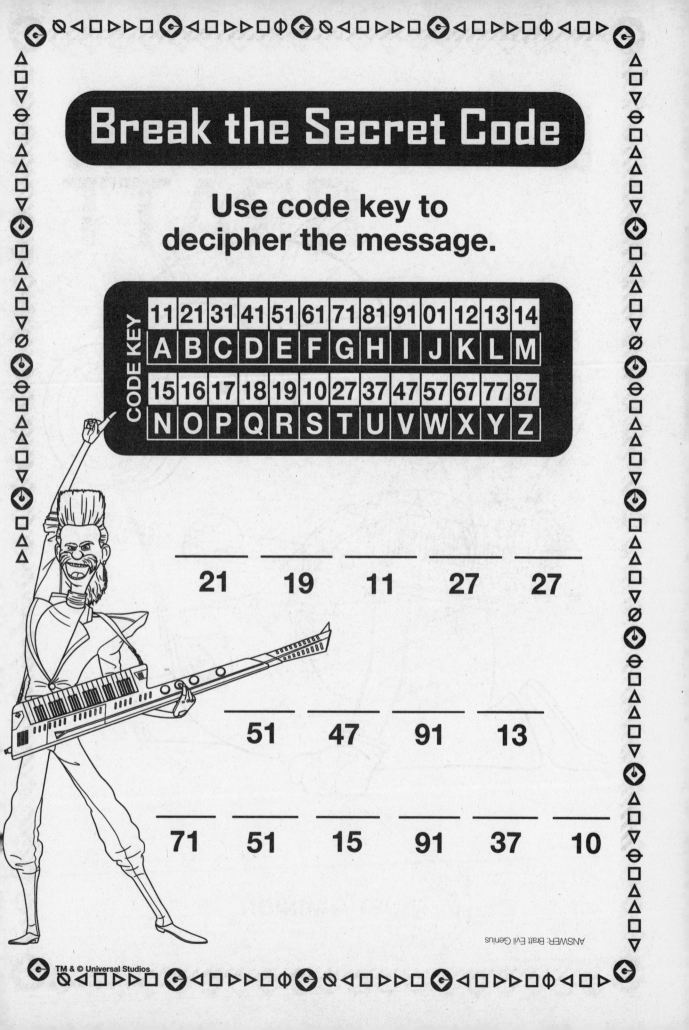

___ ___ ___ ___ ___
21   19   11   27   27

___ ___ ___ ___
51   47   91   13

___ ___ ___ ___ ___ ___
71   51   15   91   37   10

ANSWER: Bratt Evil Genius

TM & © Universal Studios

BALTHAZAR BRATT

TM & © Universal Studios

FEEL THE LOVE

TM & © Universal Studios

One In A Minion!

Draw yourself as a Minion character!

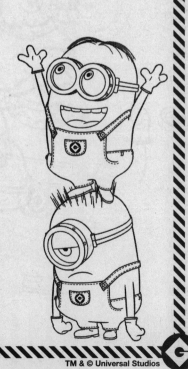

TM & © Universal Studios

Which Path?

Which line leads to Mel!

Answer:

TM & © Universal Studios

ANSWER: B

MEH...

TM & © Universal Studios

TM & © Universal Studios

AGNES

TM & © Universal Studios

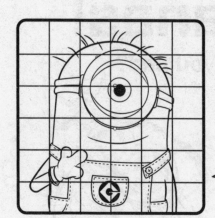

DRAW CARL

Using the grid as a guide, draw the picture in the box below.

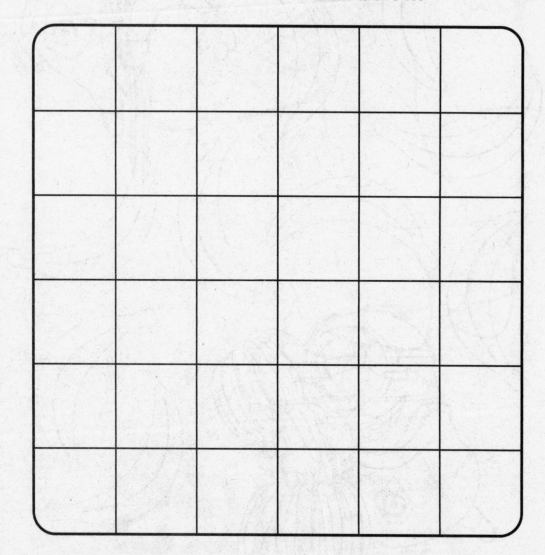

TM & © Universal Studios

Going Bananas!

How many bananas can you find?

TM & © Universal Studios

Which One?

Which Minion is different?

A.

B.

C.

D.

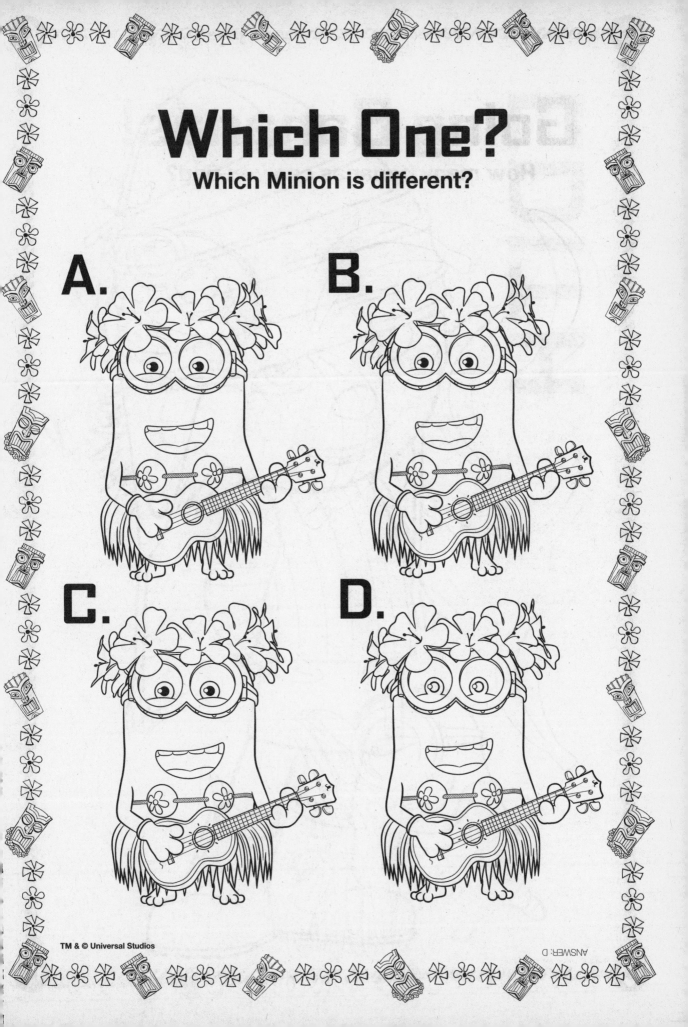

TM & © Universal Studios

ANSWER: D

EDITH

TM & © Universal Studios

Crazy Maze

Help Carl break his buddy out of jail.

START

FINISH

TM & © Universal Studios

GOAL... WORLD DOMINATION!

TM & © Universal Studios

SO CUTE!

TM & © Universal Studios

SQUARES

Taking turns, connect a line from one icon to another. Whoever makes the line that completes a box puts their initial inside the box. The person with the most squares at the end of the game wins!

example

TM & © Universal Studios

TIC#TAC#TOE

Each player will alternate putting and X or an O in any of the nine sections of the grid. The player who gets 3 in a row wins.

TM & © Universal Studios

JERRY

TM & © Universal Studios

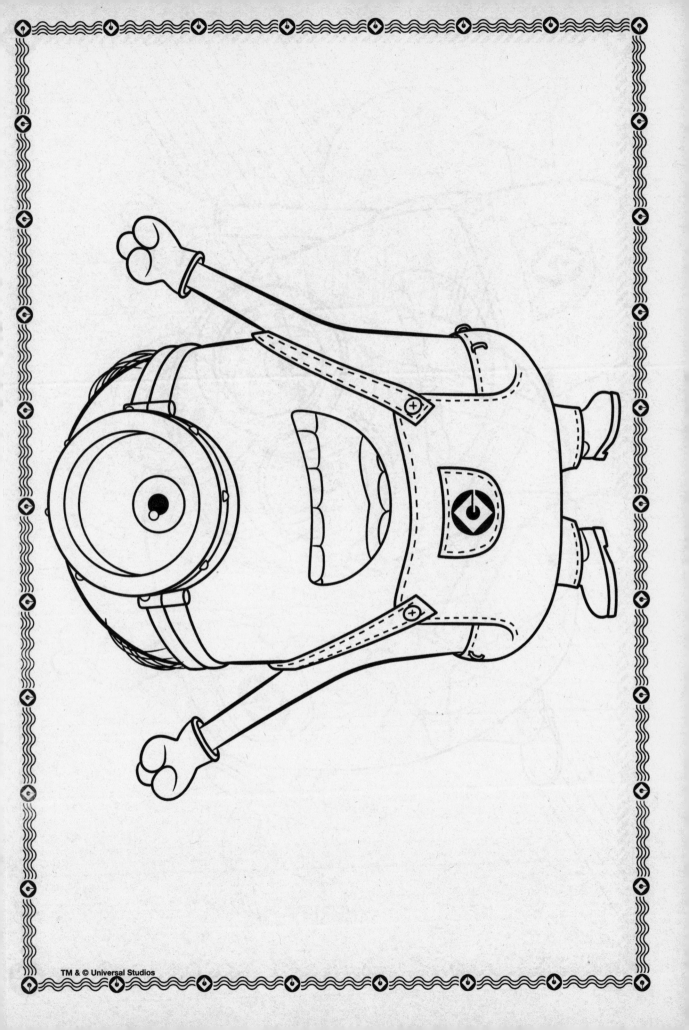

TM & © Universal Studios

TM & © Universal Studios

UNSCRAMBLE

GRU
LUCY
DESPICABLE
MARGO
AGNES
EDITH

Using the words from the list, unscramble the letters to spell the names and words.

1. ANSGE _____

2. ULYC _____

3. URG _____

4. AGRMO _____

5. EAEDLPCSIB _____

6. IETDH _____

TM & © Universal Studios

Find the Match
Find the shadow that matches Margo.

1.

2.

3.

4.

TM & © Universal Studios

ANSWER: 4

WORD SEARCH

BALTHAZAR
EVIL GENIUS
FREEDONIA
CLIVE
PIGS
DRU

R H J P U J S X I W R Y Z R C
Q D I L Z U H N V M G D U C Z
S Y Q C G X P X A R G N D S J
W N X S L S E V V O Z K U W C
N V N W E I Y K C I U I O U E
B W B Q O S V T H W N I H E F
L F A G L V J E A E D N T T A
Y R L B B B T N K G P A F F K H
I E T F Y Q J L D Q W O L W I
V E H G R V I T G R F O U I I
M D A T W V Q O G Z U L Y N F
E O Z Z E T S R H P Z U H K W
O N A E D X W C H X I E G S E
D I R Y X M I B N C Z G X G O
V A F M O E E V G G Z E S W S

TM & © Universal Studios

TM & © Universal Studios

Which Path?

Help Agnes find the path that leads her to Lucky!

A

B

C

D

E

Answer: ☐

TM & © Universal Studios

ANSWER: B

MARGO

TM & © Universal Studios

TM & © Universal Studios

Which One?

Which one of these things is Agnes' favorite?

A.

B.

C.

D.

ANSWER: D

TM & © Universal Studios

Crossword Puzzle

Using the word list, complete the crossword word puzzle below.

WORD LIST:

BANANA   AGNES   SPY

MINION   EDITH   LASER

TM & © Universal Studios

DRU

TM & © Universal Studios

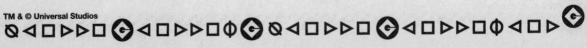

TM & © Universal Studios

GRU AND DRU ARE BROTHERS.

TM & © Universal Studios

Crazy Maze

Help Agnes through
the maze to find Fluffy!

↓
START

FINISH
↓

TM & © Universal Studios

Finish The Drawing!

Complete the drawing of Gru!

TM & © Universal Studios

WORD SEARCH

KYLE
SILAS
FRITZ
PAPOY
VALERIE
NIKO

E Y U I Z S X K Q D N J J X K
H S L U X O X W Y C I Y U U I
Z S K S Z S E S I L A S M W G
I M E E Z G O G Z K E Q R U K
Y R L A C J Q D W M Q H P B W
N P X V V N T U F T E F D V S
N G T S P A R D T R G T T J W
L D L W Y D L F F N I V S A P
C M J W G N F E C C G T M B G
G W L F N A I Z R Q K V Z F G
L X T P N D V M L I N I K O F
Y F T A Q K M V N Z E O W X M
V Y J P F S H X Q O E B S H O
B G P O H D P E B G H S D H X
I Z V V Y U N R X P R H W P D Q

TM & © Universal Studios

TM & © Universal Studios

TIC#TAC#TOE

Each player will alternate putting and X or an O in any of the nine sections of the grid. The player who gets 3 in a row wins.

TM & © Universal Studios

BA-NA-NA!

TM & © Universal Studios

TM & © Universal Studios

How many words can you make from the letters in:
DESPICABLE ME

TM & © Universal Studios

Which One?

Which Minion is different?

A.

B.

C.

D.

ANSWER: B

TM & © Universal Studios

BELLO

TM & © Universal Studios

YELLOW IS THE NEW BLACK

TM & © Universal Studios

99% ADORABLE, 1% DESPICABLE

TM & © Universal Studios

Which Path?

Which line leads to Gru!

Answer: ☐

ANSWER: B

TM & © Universal Studios

SQUARES

Taking turns, connect a line from one icon to another. Whoever makes the line that completes a box puts their initial inside the box. The person with the most squares at the end of the game wins!

example

TM & © Universal Studios

TIC#TAC#TOE

Each player will alternate putting and X or an O in any of the nine sections of the grid. The player who gets 3 in a row wins.

TM & © Universal Studios

STRIPES ARE IN

TM & © Universal Studios

DRAW EDITH

Using the grid as a guide, draw the picture in the box below.

TM & © Universal Studios

GRU AND DRU ARE COMPLETE OPPOSITES.

TM & © Universal Studios

LET'S REVOLT!

TM & © Universal Studios

UNSCRAMBLE

CARL
KEVIN
STUART
MINIONS
JERRY
DAVE

Using the words from the list, unscramble the letters to spell the names and words.

1. TSARTU

_____

2. ACLR

_____

3. EADV

_____

4. SNNOIIM

_____

5. REYRJ

_____

6. VEKNI

_____

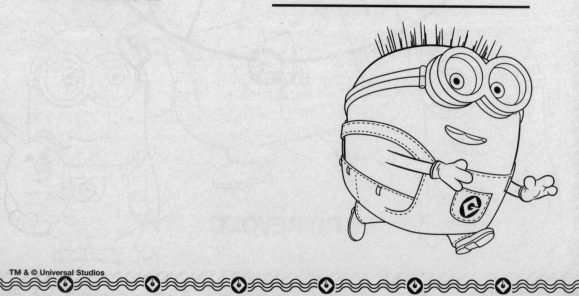

TM & © Universal Studios

Crazy Maze

Help Dave and Jerry reach
Tom at the center of the maze.

FINISH

START

TM & © Universal Studios

TM & © Universal Studios

TM & © Universal Studios

GRU

TM & © Universal Studios

Find the Match
Find the shadow that matches the Minion.

1.

2.

3.

4.

TM & © Universal Studios

ANSWER: 2

WORD SEARCH

GRU
LUCY
FAMILY
MARGO
AGNES
EDITH

T P U S B F R G Z K C X W O Q
U I U P Y P N Q I O Y T A U H
D R P J Y M O S R J V Z Z K W
G C I C B F J X B R Z M V C W
Y U E R C O A P J A H L T R K
I T R V G E G M V T D O U W H
J S W R L A O F I J X U F O V
I W A S Q T E D Z L X C W U K
R M F K A P E I B J Y W M U S
Z J D K S B F Z G Y A V H Y M
T V R E X J A V P L U P O R O
B N N H H O T V C J G Y N D T
M G I M C D N I R K W E N M O
A E Y N Q M E O Y J X L K Q R
U X X I J U L U C Y X B B X V

TM & © Universal Studios

DRAW KYLE

Using the grid as a guide, draw the picture in the box below.

TM & © Universal Studios

FEEL THE BEAT

TM & © Universal Studios

Which piece is missing?

Only one of the puzzle pieces below will fit. Can you find the missing piece and complete the puzzle?

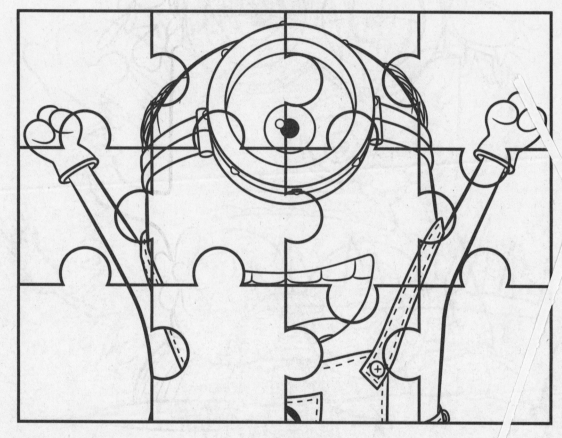

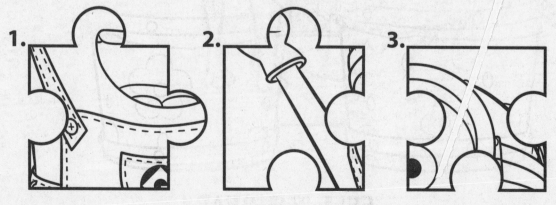

1.

2.

3.

ANSWER: 1

TM & © Universal Studios

KYLE IS GRUMPY.

TM & © Universal Studios

Which piece is missing?

Only one of the puzzle pieces below will fit. Can you find the missing piece and complete the puzzle?

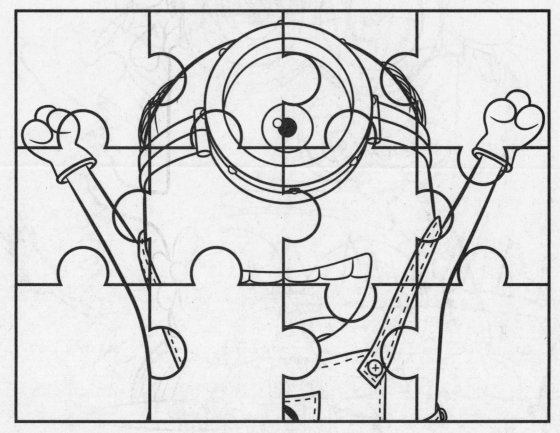

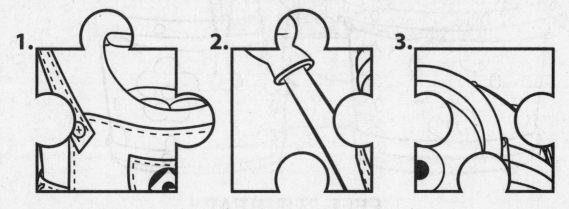

1.   **2.**   **3.**

ANSWER: 1

TM & © Universal Studios

KYLE IS GRUMPY.

TM & © Universal Studios

IT'S GOOD TO BE A MINION.

TM & © Universal Studios

Finish The Drawing!

Complete the drawing of Margo!

TM & © Universal Studios

Which Path?

Which line leads to Margo!

Ⓐ   Ⓑ   Ⓒ

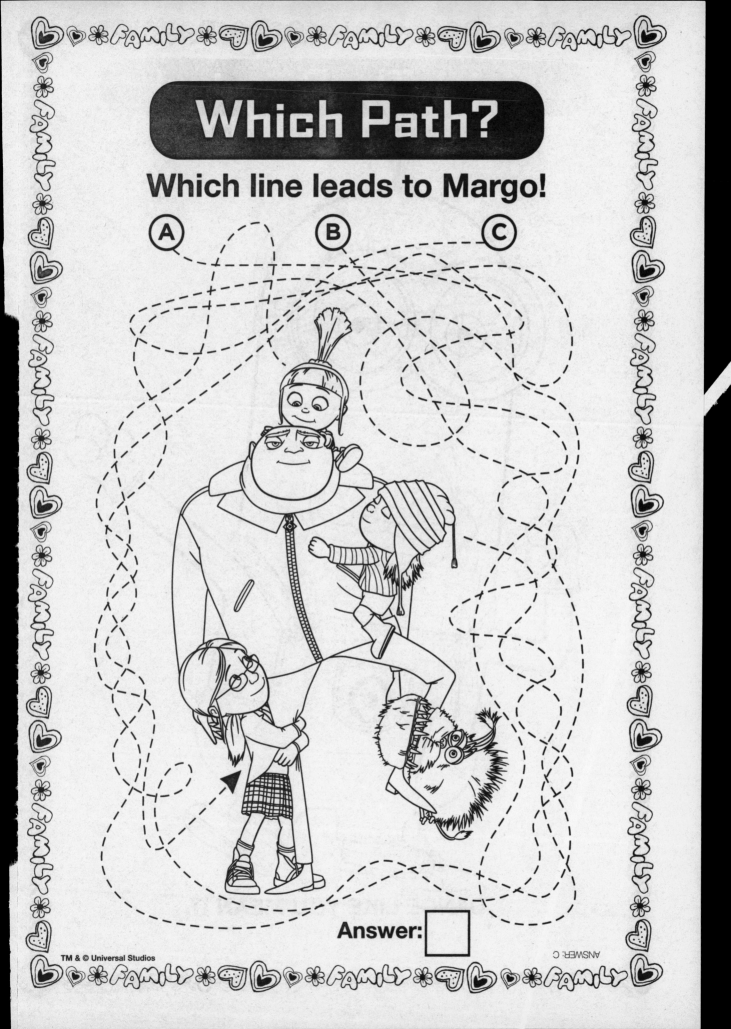

Answer:

TM & © Universal Studios

ANSWER: C

DANCE LIKE YOU MEAN IT.

TM & © Universal Studios

TM & © Universal Studios

SLURP

TM & © Universal Studios

WORD SEARCH

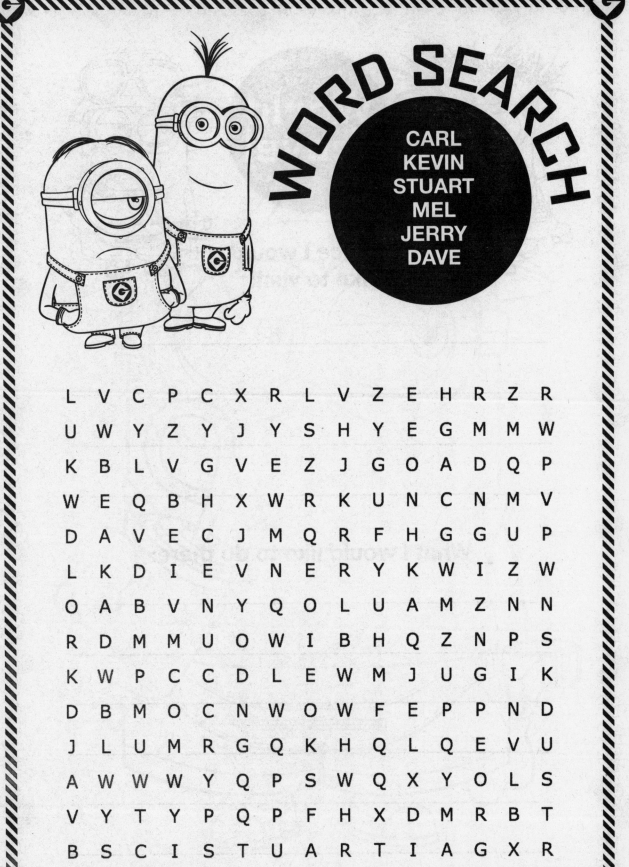

**CARL
KEVIN
STUART
MEL
JERRY
DAVE**

```
L V C P C X R L V Z E H R Z R
U W Y Z Y J J Y S H Y E G M M W
K B L V G V E Z J G O A D Q P
W E Q B H X W R K U N C N M V
D A V E C J M Q R F H G G U P
L K D I E V N E R Y K W I Z W
O A B V N Y Q O L U A M Z N N
R D M M U O W I B H Q Z N P S
K W P C C D L E W M J U G I K
D B M O C N W O W F E P P N D
J L U M R G Q K H Q L Q E V U
A W W W Y Q P S W Q X Y O L S
V Y T Y P Q P F H X D M R B T
B S C I S T U A R T I A G X R
O G Z G U C E C F H C P T M A
```

TM & © Universal Studios

World Travel

A place I would like to visit:

_____

_____

_____

_____

What I would like to do there:

_____

_____

_____

_____

_____

TM & © Universal Studios

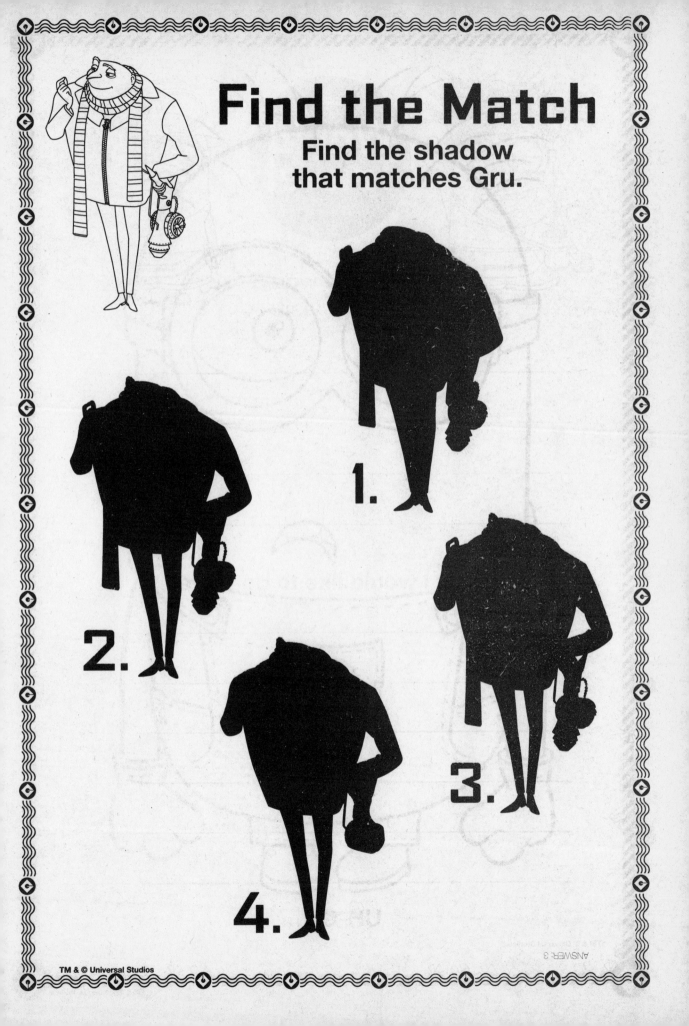

Find the Match
Find the shadow that matches Gru.

1.

2.

3.

4.

ANSWER: 3

TM & © Universal Studios

UH-OH...

TM & © Universal Studios

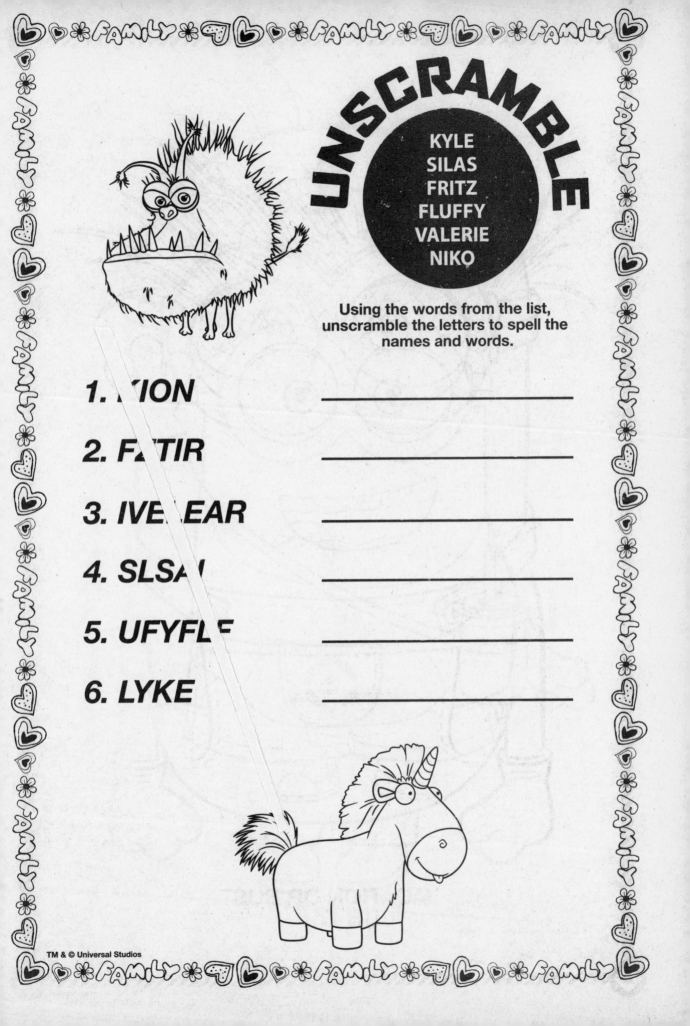

UNSCRAMBLE

KYLE
SILAS
FRITZ
FLUFFY
VALERIE
NIKO

Using the words from the list, unscramble the letters to spell the names and words.

1. NION _____

2. FRTIR _____

3. IVELEAR _____

4. SLSAI _____

5. UFYFLF _____

6. LYKE _____

TM & © Universal Studios

VACATION OR BUST

TM & © Universal Studios

CLIVE

TM & © Universal Studios

SQUARES

Taking turns, connect a line from one icon to another. Whoever makes the line that completes a box puts their initial inside the box. The person with the most squares at the end of the game wins!

example

TM & © Universal Studios

TIC#TAC#TOE

Each player will alternate putting and X or an O in any of the nine sections of the grid. The player who gets 3 in a row wins.

TM & © Universal Studios

TM & © Universal Studios

TIME TO BREAK OUT

Which One?

Which Clive is different?

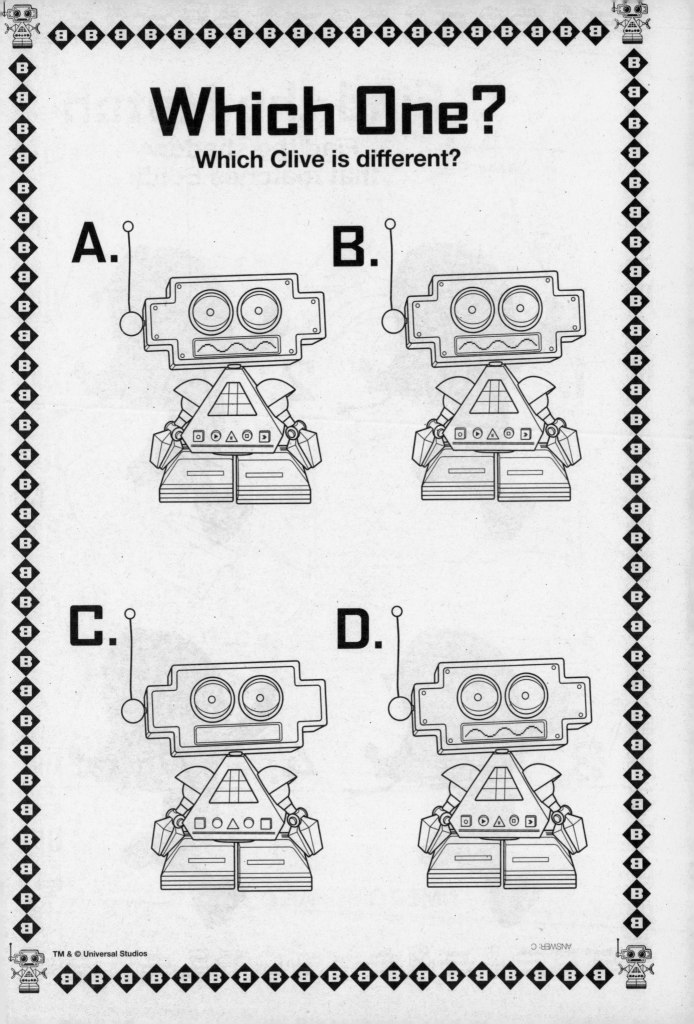

A.

B.

C.

D.

TM & © Universal Studios

ANSWER: C

Find the Match

Find the shadow
that matches Edith.

1.

2.

3.

4.

TM & © Universal Studios

ANSWER: 2

UNSCRAMBLE

BRATT
EVIL GENIUS
DOMINATION
MASTERMIND
KEYTAR
CLIVE

Using the words from the list, unscramble the letters to spell the names and words.

1. TBRTA _____

2. VEILC _____

3. ELVI SINGEU _____

4. RTYAEK _____

5. IERMDATSNM _____

6. MTOODNAINI _____

TM & © Universal Studios

YELLOW BELLO

TM & © Universal Studios

SQUARES

Taking turns, connect a line from one icon to another. Whoever makes the line that completes a box puts their initial inside the box. The person with the most squares at the end of the game wins!

example

TM & © Universal Studios

TM & © Universal Studios

TM & © Universal Studios

How many words can you make from the letters in:
GRU'S CREW

_____   _____

_____   _____

_____   _____

_____

_____

_____

_____

_____

_____

_____

_____

TM & © Universal Studios

DRAW LUCY

Using the grid as a guide, draw the picture in the box below.

TM & © Universal Studios

I'VE GOT MOVES YOU HAVE NEVER SEEN.

TM & © Universal Studios

TM & © Universal Studios

TM & © Universal Studios

Crazy Maze

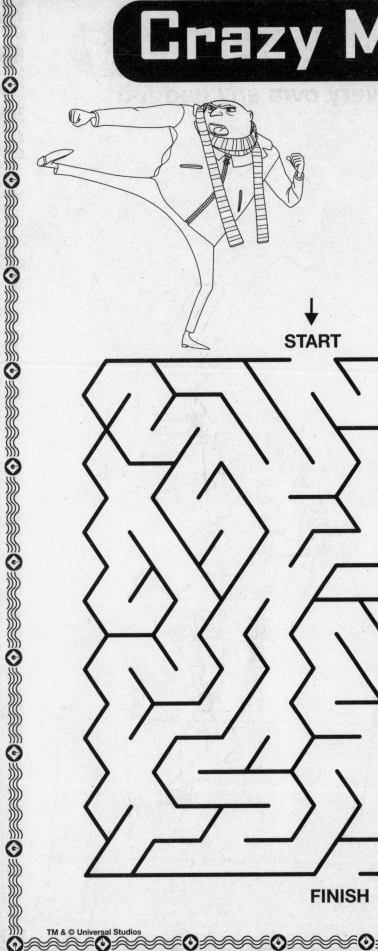

Help Gru through the maze!

↓

START

FINISH

TM & © Universal Studios

What's Your Spy Gadget?

Draw your very own spy gadget!

TM & © Universal Studios